I LOVE MYTHOLOGY

Odyssey

(The Adventures of Odysseus)

Text: Anastasia D. Makri
Illustration: Akis Melachris
Translated from Greek into English
Kiriaki Papakonstantinou
BA English Language & Literature / MA Psycholinguistics / DIPTRANS - DPSI
Chartered Linguist (Translator) / Translators - Interpreters Trainer
Member of the Chartered Institute of Linguists in London

UNDER THE AEGIS OF

ΟΜΙΛΟΣ ΓΙΑ ΤΗΝ UNESCO ΝΟΜΟΥ ΠΕΙΡΑΙΩΣ & ΝΗΣΩΝ
CLUB FOR UNESCO OF THE DEPARTMENT OF PIRAEUS & ISLANDS
Πέτρου Ράλλη 210 & Θησέως 1 Νίκαια,
Τηλ.: 210 4967757, Fax: 210 4944564 - www.unescopireas.gr e-mail: unescop@otenet.gr

United Nations
Educational, Scientific
& Cultural Organization

AGYRA
publications

The War of Troy

Ten years had passed before the end of the Trojan War. This war broke out with the abduction of Helen – the most beautiful of all women and wife of Menelaus, King of Sparta – by Paris, the son of King Priam of Troy. Greeks were the winners of the war. After many battles and thousands people dead and wounded, they managed to enter the city of Troy, despite its mighty walls. The Greek who achieved this was the ingenious King of Ithaca, Odysseus. He came up with the idea to build a huge wooden horse, the Trojan Horse, which the Greeks one night left outside the walls of Troy. The next morning, the camp and the ships of the Greeks were gone. The Trojans believed that the Greeks finally retreated. As far as the wooden horse is concerned, they considered it a good sign from the gods and hauled it inside the walls. Yet, in the wooden horse Greek soldiers were hidden. So, when the Trojans finished the celebrations and the whole city fell into a deep sleep, the Greeks came out of the horse, opened the gates and let their army rush into the walls.

Nothing was left in place. The city was looted and burned down.

The Trojans tried to defend themselves, but the Greeks killed almost everyone. The war was over; the Greeks took Helen back and could at last return home. However, it would be too long before Odysseus reached his homeland ...

The Journey Begins

The journey home began along with storms, which forced Odysseus' ships to change direction and reach the land of Cicones, allies of the Trojans. Odysseus' men wanted to conquer the island – Ismarus – but Odysseus did not agree. Eventually, after loosing several men they sailed off defeated. As if this was not enough, they had not sailed far when a bitter north wind began to roar over the open sea. The sails of the boats were torn apart; only the oars were left. They wandered like this for days pushed far off their course, until they reached an unknown land, where they went ashore to rest on the beach. Odysseus sent three companions to explore the place with caution. Some time later, they met some locals who offered them a strange but delicious fruit, called lotus.

Odysseus' companions ate to their heart's content.

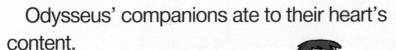

Yet, whoever ate this fruit would forget their desire to return home. Odysseus, seeing they were late, went in search of his companions, only to find them in stupefied bliss. He realized what had happened, tied them up and dragged them back to the ship. So, they managed to sail away together from the land of the Lotus-Eaters.

Polyphemus, the Cyclops[*]

O dysseus and his men had been at sea for a while until they were brought to the Island of Cyclops, which seemed de-

* Cyclops: The Cyclops were mythical creatures of the Greek and Roman mythology who had one eye in the middle of the forehead. The word Cyclops comes from the combination of two words: cycle and ophtalmos (i.e. eye, in ancient Greek). The Cyclops in Odyssey were sons of the god Poseidon.

4

serted. On top of a hill there stood an inviting cave. Odysseus took some of his companions and a flask full of wine and set out to explore the cave. When they reached the entrance of the cave, Odysseus shouted: "Is anybody here?" There was no reply. So, they all entered the cave with precaution. There, they found sheep and goats penned in some big bowls, like those used for milk coagulation to make cheese. They were all too hungry that stuffed themselves full. Suddenly, a deafening sound was heard. At the entrance of the cave stood a huge, one-eyed Cyclops followed by a flock of sheep. After the sheep entered the cave, the Cyclops closed the entrance with a giant boulder. Then his single eye fell upon Odysseus and his companions. "Who are you?" he asked in a thunderous voice that made them paralyze by fear. "We are warriors, and we come from Troy. The storm threw us in your island and we beg you to help us" replied Odysseus.

"Who cares to help you" said the Cyclops and immediately grabbed two of the men and ate them up. Then, after drinking plenty of milk, he fell in deep sleep. The next morning the Cyclops left once more with his sheep and closed the cave with the huge rock. Immediately Odysseus asked his men to find a long stake and had one of its ends sharpened. On his return in the afternoon, the Cyclops devoured two more men. Then Odysseus, stifling his anger, offered him a cup of wine. The Cyclops drank it at once and Odysseus refilled it. "What's your name?" asked the Cyclops. "My name is No One" replied Odysseus. Soon the

5

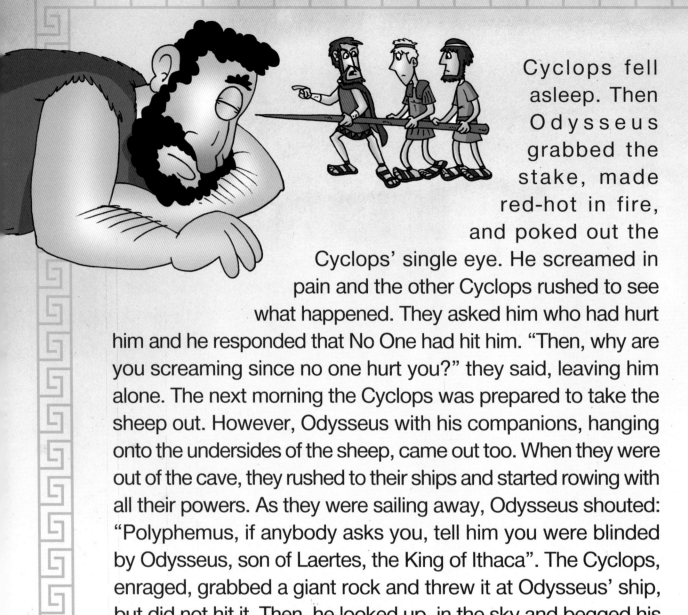

Cyclops fell asleep. Then Odysseus grabbed the stake, made red-hot in fire, and poked out the Cyclops' single eye. He screamed in pain and the other Cyclops rushed to see what happened. They asked him who had hurt him and he responded that No One had hit him. "Then, why are you screaming since no one hurt you?" they said, leaving him alone. The next morning the Cyclops was prepared to take the sheep out. However, Odysseus with his companions, hanging onto the undersides of the sheep, came out too. When they were out of the cave, they rushed to their ships and started rowing with all their powers. As they were sailing away, Odysseus shouted: "Polyphemus, if anybody asks you, tell him you were blinded by Odysseus, son of Laertes, the King of Ithaca". The Cyclops, enraged, grabbed a giant rock and threw it at Odysseus' ship, but did not hit it. Then, he looked up, in the sky and begged his father, the god Poseidon, to punish Odysseus for the hurt he had done and pass through great ordeal before he gets home.

Aeolus and the Bag of Winds

The next stop of Odysseus and his companions was Aeolia. Aeolus, the god keeper of the winds, who generously offered his hospitality, was king there. When they decided to continue their journey, Aeolus gave Odysseus a leather bag. "This sack contains all the storm winds. I let out only the sea breeze, the gentle breeze to sail back home. Beware, though, Odysseus, do not open the bag because the strong winds will break free and things will be very bad for you". Odysseus thanked him, took the bag and they sailed off with their sails lifted.

Curiosity, however, forced his men to see what was inside the bag. One night, while Odysseus was asleep, someone suggested opening the bag. They believed they would find a rare treasure inside. Once the bag was opened, all the fretful winds rushed out and a furious storm hit them. The sea was fierce and sky-high waves rose. Odysseus woke up and felt very embittered about what had happened. The waves brought them back to the island of Aeolus who, realized what had happened, got angry and send them away.

7

In the Land of Laestrygonians

Odysseus, with his soul full of sorrow, left Aeolia with his companions. They had been rowing for days until they reached the island of the Laestrygonians. There, smoke was coming out of the earth and the soil was not plowed at all. On arriving there, all the other ships entered the harbor; all except Odysseus' ship which was anchored outside the harbor, near a lighthouse. There they were attacked by the Laestrygonians, a ferocious people, who hurled huge stones onto the sailors. Nobody survived the onslaught of the Laestrygonians. Only Odysseus' ship managed to flee away, as it remained outside the harbor, and Odysseus cut the rope saving his own self and the only men who remained alive.

At the Palace of Circe

With a heavy heart and lamenting the loss of so many companions, a long time later they reached the island of Aeaea. Odysseus sent some men, led by Eurylochus, to find food and water. They reached a hill and saw a marble palace standing on it. Soon a beautiful woman appeared before them, who said in a smile: "I am Circe and I am happy to welcome you in my palace". The men surprised followed her and she led them to a room where they were given plenty of food to eat and a sweet wine to drink; yet, the wine contained magical herbs. However, Eurylochus neither ate nor drank anything. He remained hidden in a corner watching everything that was going on. Once the men had finished eating, Circe touched them with her wand and turned them into pigs. Then, she penned them up. Once Eurylochus saw this, he started running as if he had wings on his feet. He had to find Odysseus as soon as possible and tell him the bad news.

When Odysseus heard what had happened, he took his sword and spear and asked Eurylochus to show him the way. "Please, Brave Odysseus, do not go. I'm afraid you will not come back. This woman is beautiful yet cunning". Odysseus, however,

9

did not listen to him and immediately set out to save his companions.

On his way, Hermes appeared before him. "Take this flower sent by the goddess Athena, and the Circe's spell will not affect you" he said.

Odysseus thanked Hermes, ate the flower and continued his way. On arriving at the palace, Circe came out to welcome him. He followed her and entered the palace. Circe offered him food and, of course, gave him sweet wine to drink, which contained her magical herbs. But when she touched him with her wand, Odysseus not only was not turned into a pig, but lunged over and put his sharp sword on her throat. "Take me right now to my men" he said.

Circe, startled and surprised, led Odysseus to a field full of pigs. "Cast off your spell immediately" Odysseus ordered Circe. She rubbed the pigs with a magic herb and turned them into humans again. His companions, weeping with emotion, fell into Odysseus' arms. Circe invited them all to stay in her palace, after promising that she would not try to cast any other spells on them. Indeed, all of Odysseus' men, along with those who were waiting in the ship, went to the palace and had a great time; and time was just flowing away. However, homesickness would not leave Odysseus' heart. So, one day, he asked Circe to help them leave. She accepted, although her heart was full of love for him. She told him, however, that they had to descend to the underworld to get a prophecy* from Teiresias, the seer. On hearing her words Odysseus' heart was all tightened up. How was he supposed to tell this to his way worn companions?

Indeed, when Odysseus announced to his men what would follow, they were frozen by fear. When they approached the edge of the ocean, where the land of the Cimmerians was, the sky was wrapped in mist. Soon they reached the entrance to Hades. There Odysseus made sacrifices to the dead pouring on top honey, milk

and flour. In a while, the seer Teiresias appeared in front of him and started talking about the things to come. He said he will anticipate many difficulties, because Poseidon was angry with him for blinding his son. But eventually he will reach home.

---

* Prophecy: it is the response of the oracle** to anyone asking for advice on what to do or what was going to happen in the future. Prophecies were given by priestess Pythia.

** Oracle: The oracle was the place where people communicated with gods and asked for a prophecy. At the oracle, gods approved or disapproved of people's actions and gave advice on what to do in the future.

On finishing his words, Teiresias disappeared. Then, Odysseus ordered his men to return to the island of Circe, who was all too happy to welcome them. Actually, she advised Odysseus what to do when they would reach the Sirens, Scylla and Charybdis, as well as the island of the Sun.

The Sirens

At dawn, they set off on their journey. Odysseus told his companions that when they were about to reach the Sirens they should fill their ears with wax, because those who listened to their song were enchanted and great disaster would come on them. His curiosity got the better of him though, and he ordered his crew to tie him to the mast, saying that no matter how much he begged them to untie him, they should ignore him.

When they reached the Sirens, their enchanting voices were trying to seduce them; but the crew was not listening. Odysseus, fascinated by the lovely song, was striving to be released from the ropes that kept him tied up to the mast, shouting at his men to untie him; but they did not hear him at all. Only when they were far enough from those magical creatures did they untie Odysseus and remove the wax from their ears.

Scylla and Charybdis

Their journey continued, yet a great danger was before them. They had to sail through a narrow strait and pass between tall and sharp rocks. On the one side lived a horrifying monster, Charybdis, which would swallow water and ships three times a day. No ship passing by was ever saved.

Once they entered the strait, Odysseus shouted, "Hurry up! To the oars with all your strength!" Then he tried to get the ship as closer to the rocks as possible, trying to avoid the monster. But on the opposite side there was Scylla, a six-headed monster, which grabbed six of Odysseus' men and devoured them. Odysseus remained cool and, without leaving the oars from his hands, managed to get out of that terrible place and escape with the rest of his companions.

The Cattle of Helios

They continued their journey until they finally arrived at the Island of Helios to have a rest. Numerous cattle were grazing there. Odysseus remembered Circe's advice and told his men: "These cattle belong to Helios, the Sun god, and are sacred. Nobody should hurt them".

The men seemed to obey this order. One day, however, the famished men recklessly slaughtered and ate some cattle, while Odysseus was away.

When Odysseus came back and saw what had happened, he felt that a great misfortune would fall on them. Indeed, Helios was so angry that he asked Zeus to cast on them a harsh punishment.

Odysseus ordered his men to get ready to sail away as fast as possible. However, when they were at the open sea, the sky darkened and a tremendous storm broke out. The winds were blowing so hard that the rigging of the ship was broken and soon, a strong thunderbolt struck the ship. The whole crew was drowned. The only survivor was Odysseus who managed to grab the upturned keel of the ship. He struggled with the waves for several days, until eventually he was carried to a beautiful island.

Goddess Calypso

The all beautiful goddess Calypso lived on this island. She loved Odysseus with all her heart. Her greatest desire was he never left her. But Odysseus was tortured by his longing to return home. The goddess Athena decided to beg Zeus to help him. So, Zeus sent Hermes, who persuaded Calypso to help Odysseus return home.

Calypso, despite her sadness for being parted from her beloved Odysseus, helped him build a boat and said goodbye with a heavy heart.

At first his journey was peaceful. But after a few days, the god Poseidon unleashed a big storm. He had not forgotten that Odysseus had hurt his son, the Cyclops. Odysseus' boat was broken and once again he had to struggle with the waves. It was hours before the wrecked hero reached a shore. With all his strength, he crept up the coast, where exhausted fell into deep sleep. He barely managed to hide his naked body with some olive branches.

The Island of the Phaeacians

Odysseus was on the island of the Phaeacians, the kingdom of King Alcinous, who had a beautiful daughter, Nausicaa.

Indeed, she was the one who found him sleeping on the sand. She went there along with her handmaidens to wash clothes in the river and then play with the ball. Their laughter and voices woke Odysseus up, who appeared before them, hiding his naked body with an olive branch and asked for help. All the girls were shocked, except Nausicaa, who was advised by the goddess Athena. Nausicaa ordered her handmaidens to bathe, dress and feed him well in order to regain his strength. Then, she asked Odysseus to follow them to the palace from a distance. There, he would ask the help from her mother, Queen Arete and her father, King Alcinous. On seeing them, Odysseus fell on their feet and begged them to help him return home.

The king generously offered him his hospitality and Odysseus touched by such a welcoming narrated his adventures.

17

His audience, surprised, felt honored to meeting the famous hero. Immediately, King Alcinous ordered to have a ship prepared to get Odysseus back home.

Returning Home

The next morning Odysseus thanked Alcinous for his warm hospitality and went aboard. He was exhausted yet excited. During the journey, he fell into a sweet sleep. When he arrived in Ithaca, the sailors took him carefully ashore and left him sleeping on the sand. Then, they sailed back to their island.

Odysseus woke up in a dense fog. He could not see clearly around him and could not understand where he was. Then, the goddess Athena, transformed into a young shepherd, was presented in front of him. "Do not worry, Odysseus. You are in your island", she said. Odysseus immediately kneeled and with eyes full of tears kissed the soil of his homeland. At that point, the goddess regained her normal figure and told him what he should do. Then she touched him with her wand and transformed him into a beggar.

As Athena had advised him, Odysseus went to find Eumaeus, the swineherd. On arriving at his hut, Eumaeus welcomed him without recognizing him. After they had finished their meal, Eumaeus started telling him his sorrows; about king Odysseus, who was lost; about the queen, Penelope, who waited for her husband and suffered day after day as she could not get over her heartache; about the roister suitors who were wasting the king's property, even pushing Penelope to choose one of them for her husband; and, last but not least, about the prince, Telemachus, who left to Pylos to flee from the suitors who threatened his life.

While Eumaeus was talking, the door opened and a well-built lad appeared on the doorstep. "Welcome Telemachus", cried Eumaeus who immediately rushed to hug him. "Thank you, my dear friend", replied Telemachus. "I want you to go and find my mother and tell her that I am here. Nobody else knows about my return". In a while Eumaeus went to the palace and Odysseus got out of the hut, where the goddess Athena gave him his normal figure. On seeing him, Telemachus was astonished. "Who are you?" he asked full of surprise. "I am your father, my son", replied Odysseus excited and took him in his arms. Father and son stayed like that

19

for hours, weeping with joy. Then, they started planning how they would anticipate the suitors. The next morning, Telemachus went to the palace first; then Odysseus  followed dressed as a beggar, along with Eumaeus.

When they arrived at the palace, Odysseus saw his beloved dog, Argus. The dog was too old; yet, on seeing Odysseus he started wagging his tail with all his strength and, looking at his master with love, he died. Odysseus' eyes got bleary and covered his face not to show his emotions. Then, he entered the palace where the suitors had started junketing. Odysseus begged for some food from the suitors and they threw their leftovers at him. One of the suitors, Antinous, actually treated Odysseus wrong by throwing a chair at him. Penelope, who learned about such wrong behavior to the stranger, asked to meet him. When the beggar, Odysseus, stood in front of her she asked him who he was and where he was from. Odysseus looked at her with eyes full of tears and said: "Do not ask me this, my fair lady, because my soul gets filled with sadness". Then, Penelope continued with tears in her eyes: "My heart, stranger, is also full of pain. I haven not seen my beloved husband for years. I do not know if he is dead or alive. And on top of all this, in order to get rid of the suitors I have told them I would choose one of them for my new husband after I was done weaving a shawl for Laertes, Odysseus' father. I would weave all day and unweave the shawl at night. This way time passes by; but until when? Tell me, though, do you know anything about Odysseus?"

"Do not worry, my beautiful and faithful Penelope. Your husband will come back" said Odysseus and she wished his words come true. Then, she called Eurycleia, Odysseus' old nurse, to tend him. On seeing him, she felt there was something strange about him. Many things on the beggar reminded her of Odysseus, whom she had raised. But when she started washing his feet, she saw a mark on his knee from a wound since childhood. She raised her head, looked at him with love and said: "Dear Odysseus, it is you. I was right the moment I saw you" – and delighted she wanted to share the good news with Penelope. Then Odysseus grabbed her hand and said: "My dear Eurycleia, do not tell anyone about my return. I must first clear our land of the suitors". Then, the old nanny told him not to worry and she would keep his secret.

The next morning, the suitors were gathered in the palace. They were angry because they were almost sure that Penelope was befooling them. Odysseus heard them talking of her; yet, with a heavy heart he did not say a word. Soon Penelope came holding a huge bow. "This was my husband's, Odysseus, bow. Whichever one of you manages to grip and string it and then shoot an arrow through the holes of twelve axes, all in a row, he will become my new husband", she said in a loud voice. "Let's start", said Antinous and one by one was trying his luck with the bow, but no one was successful. Meanwhile, Odysseus revealed himself to Eumaeus and Philoetius, who was the master of the apprentices, and asked them to close the doors, hide the suitors' weapons and fetch his bow and arrows. When the suitors had finished their attempts, Odysseus asked to be allowed to shoot an arrow, too. The suitors started mocking him. Telemachus, however, ordered to give him the bow and asked his mother to go to her room.

On his first attempt, Odysseus managed to pass the arrow through the holes of the twelve axes. The suitors were left speechless with amazement. Immediately, Odysseus put off his old clothes and everyone now could see in front of him a string and determined ruler. And before realizing, in terror, that King Odysseus was standing in front of them, several suitors had already been killed with his arrows. The others, terrified and armless, tried to escape but the doors were locked. Odysseus and his son, Telemachus, with Eumaeus and Philoetius on their side, left no one of them alive.

With Penelope, at last

When the palace was cleaned of the suitors, old Eurycleia rushed to tell the news to Penelope. She could not believe her ears and ran down to the big hall to find Odysseus. On seeing him, she remained speechless, unable to believe she was standing in front of her beloved husband. However, in an attempt to be sure, she decided to test him and asked Eurycleia to move their bed from their bedroom and make it with embroidered sheets. Then Odysseus, looking at her with love, said: "Nobody can move our bed. It is built on a sturdy olive trunk. Our bedroom was built around this rooted olive tree".

On hearing these words, Penelope rushed into his arms. The happiness they both felt could not be described even with a thousand words. As for Odysseus, he finally was calm and happy with his family and could not wait to start telling them of his incredible adventures.

24

Ithaca

The myth of Odysseus inspired one of the greatest Greek poets to write one of his most beautiful poems, entitled "Ithaca".

The main idea of this poem is the significance of someone to have a purpose in life and make efforts to reach it with all his powers. Through these efforts experience and knowledge is gained. All too often, yet, one can gain things much more valuable than the original aim.

Put the letters in the correct order,
to see who this poet is.

Crossword

Can you solve the above crossword?

Across

1. A faithful slave.
2. A loyal dog.
3. An ingenious and storm-tossed king.
4. They were pushing Penelope to get married.

Down

5. Odysseus' son.
6. It should pass through the holes of axes.
7. Odysseus was a king there.
8. The name of the faithful swineherd.
9. Odysseus' father.
10. The wife of the King of Ithaca.

Combination

Combine the words in column A with the words in column B.

A	B
1. Teiresias	**a.** ... swallowed the sea water.
2. Polyphemus	**b.** ... was tied up on the mast.
3. Helios	**c.** ... was a cattle owner.
4. Sirens	**d.** ... lived in the Underworld.
5. Charybdis	**e.** ... had six heads.
6. Scylla	**f.** ... sung lovely.
7. Odysseus	**g.** ... was the Poseidon's son.

1 ......   2 ......   3 ......   4 ......

5 ......   6 ......   7 ......

Combine the following:

Penelope	ingenious
Odysseus	faithful
Companions	helpful
Polyphemus	unwise
Suitors	violent
Telemachus	provocative

Pictures 2 and 3 have 3 differences each with Picture 1.
Can you spot them?

Connect the dots from 1 to 45
to see what is the hidden picture.

Can you find out which is
the shadow of Penelope?

All Circe's pigs have their pair, except one.
Can you find it?

SOLUTIONS

Page 25 CAVAFY.

Page 26

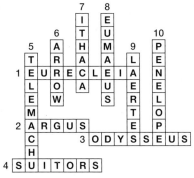

Page 27

1. = d
2. = g
3. = c
4. = f
5. = a
6. = e
7. = b

Penelope = faithful
Odysseus = ingenious
Companions = unwise
Polyphemus = violent
Suitors = provocative
Telemachus = helpful

Page 28

Page 29

Page 30 Shadow No 3.

Page 31